D0518708

THE TRUTH ABOUT TROLLS

In the many folk tales that the Icelanders tell, the average troll is almost always depicted as a nasty, evil ogre plagued with a seemingly endless agressive streak, the kind of figure that exists only in your worst nightmares.

The truth is that this shameful image is little more than an entertaining piece of fiction that probably says more about the ignorance of the storyteller than it does about the troll.

Trolls have always been feared because of the tremendous strength and enormous size that they have been gifted with. Bearing this in mind, it is quite easy to understand why humans make up negative stories about the basically harmless and inherently loveable troll. By nature, trolls are large, nocturnal, and essentially peaceful cave-dwellers. They used to spend much more time above ground, but that was many centuries ago, before Ingólfur Arnarson and his kinsmen set foot on this island. After their first catastrophic encounters with these people, the Icelandic trolls became even more wary of meeting humans than humans are of meeting trolls. Nowadays, any troll in his right mind will only venture outside his cave with extreme caution – and under cover of darkness. In the following pages, the intention is to give an accurate portrayal of the habitat and lifestyle of the remarkable Icelandic troll: an amicable, forgotten anthropoid that is (not so distantly) related to Homo sapiens – you and me.

TROLL CHILDREN

The production and rearing of children is something about which trolls take great care. Trolls can reach several hundred years of age (in human terms), and a great deal of time tends to pass between the births of children in a troll family. This is not only due to troll sleeping patterns. Trolls are very aware of the dangers of overpopulation – especially in their environment and keep a constant eye on the number of troll children being born each century. (Some of the inhabitants of the teeming surface world might do well to follow their example.)

Troll children are not only fewer in number than human children, but also take somewhat longer to grow up. They don't learn to walk until they are ten (human) years old, and it is another ten years until they begin to talk.

For the first fifty years of their lives, all troll children are brought up together in a communal children's crèche, where aged troll men and women take turns at looking after them – when they aren't taking naps.

The periods of time that trolls spend asleep gradually extend as trolls get older. The oldest often drop off for several years at a time, while young troll children rarely sleep for more than a few weeks. In the sunless world of the trolls, however, day and night are relatively meaningless concepts. Their world runs according to ideas quite different to ours, and everyone simply has his/her own time for sleeping and waking.

Comparative sizes at similar stages of childhood development. The troll child is about ten human years old, and the human baby six months of age.

The troll children shown here are eighteen years old. They are happy and red-faced in spite of never having seen the sun. Troll children commonly develop hair on their chests at a very early stage. Some are born totally covered in hair.

Most female trolls actually look like this most of the time, so it can often be difficult to tell if a female is pregnant or not. Pregnancy is thought to last five times as long as it does for humans.

AN AUTHENTIC ICELANDIC FOLK TALE

In ancient times, there was a troll woman who lived in Skessuhellir (Ogress' Cave) in Húsagil in the Mývatn district. One time she went out beachcombing, and on the way home she suddenly went into labour. She lay down by a big rock on the Sólheimar Sand, and gave birth to her child. A man came upon her, and she asked him to assist her. The man did so. His hands were soon covered with blood, but she said that he would be all the stronger for that. This rock has since been called Skessusteinn (Ogress' Rock).

Troll children enjoy sleeping every bit as much as adults do. With them, however, it is more of a communal pastime. They adore snuggling up together in great snoring, snuffling heaps, a great source of entertainment for those elders with a good sense of humour.

Troll toys are similar to those that we know and love. They even have their equivalents of Barbie and Ken.

TROLL WISDOM

Certain troll women command unlimited respect in Icelandic troll society. These are the aged sorceresses, or "Wise Ones", who over the centuries have picked up all kinds of knowledge. These women are the keepers of the ancient wisdom that was gathered by the generations of trolls that first inhabited the island.

People who have been out late on spring or autumn evenings have sometimes talked of hearing a faint thunder from the distant mountains. This may well have been a sorceress passing by, collecting the various kinds of herbs, lichen and mosses that she needs for the magic potions and medical ointments she skilfully concocts in her cave.

The sorceresses are invaluable to the other trolls who look to these women for good, sound advice and medical help. Trolls are, on the whole, a very healthy bunch. The bacteria and viruses that trouble humans so much have yet to reach the subterranean caverns that the trolls inhabit. When really drastic remedies are needed, however, the local sorceress sends her pet raven off to a distant mountain peak to collect the rare ingredients that are required. These secret and inaccessible places are the source of a number of rare mountain berries and potent medicinal herbs that the sorceresses use for their work.

Moon-glasses make it possible to wander around outside even on nights when the moon is full.

The same family of ravens have been bred and cared for by the sorceresses for thousands of years.

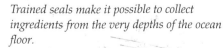

Trained seals make it possible to collect ingredients from the very depths of the ocean floor.

The sorceresses
are responsible
for the design
and creation
of the personal
lucky talismans
or amulets
worn by many
trolls. These
are guaranteed
to ward off both
evil spirits and
human beings.
The amulet at
the top, although it looks like the sun, is
in fact a representation of the full moon,
a naturally powerful force for trolls. The
lower amulet is designed to bring forth
the powers of the earth.

Troll potions
exist for all kinds of
ailments ranging from
persistent grumpiness
and sleeplessness, to bed
sores and bumped heads.

TROLL FASHION

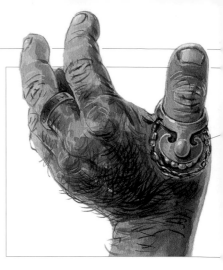

Iceland is a volcanic island, and if you go down far enough, you are sooner or later bound to come across molten rock or magma. Thanks to this cheap, if somewhat dangerous, form of central heating, the underground tunnels and chambers inhabited by trolls are always wonderfully warm, no matter what season it is. As a result, there is no obvious reason for trolls to wear clothes at all. That they do so is mainly for reasons of decency and vanity. As we have said before, trolls are very proud creatures, and even though it might not be obvious to us, they take great pains with their appearance and try to be distinctive in whatever they do.

Each troll designs and makes his or her own clothes. Unlike humans who mass-produce shirts and trousers by the thousand, and only feel comfortable if they are wearing clothes similar to everybody else´s, trolls take pride in their individuality. There are no mirrors in troll chambers. There is no need for them. Each troll is totally convinced that he or she is just right, and therefore has no need of confirmation from a bit of reflective glass.

Material is spun and woven using the same ancient methods as those employed by Icelanders centuries ago. Indeed, it has been suggested that humans might have learnt some of these skills from the trolls. Natural colours, like blond, brown, black, white and grey (found in abundance) are favoured by trolls because they do not fade and it is important that they stand the test of time.
Occasionally, however, mineral dyes are employed for the sake of variety.

Trolls are also highly adept at fashioning things out of metal, and they pride themselves on their skill at making brooches and buckles. Painstaking attention is always applied to every detail.

Troll cloth is woven entirely from troll hair which is both extremely tough and hard-wearing. Troll hair keeps on growing all the time while they are asleep, and since trolls tend to sleep for long periods of time, there is always more than enough excess hair lying around that can easily be utilised. Nonetheless, trolls have a principle of only harvesting what they need, and no more. Since it is considered extremely bad manners to disturb a slumbering troll, all harvesting is done as gently as possible.

Very rarely do trolls wear anything on their feet, even when venturing onto the glaciers in wintertime. Those few trolls that do wear shoes, make them from toughened mushroom skins.

TROLL CUISINE

The main source of troll nutrition is almost exclusively fish. The local sorceress concocts a secret bait for trolls that fish seem to find utterly irresistible. In consequence, a single troll can haul in vast quantities of fish in a very short period of time. Indeed, when Icelanders start complaining about fish shortages and start imposing quotas on the fishing fleet, it's usually because, as sometimes happens, a large proportion of the famished troll population has woken up at the same time

Trolls enjoy eating their fish raw, sushi style. For variety, however, when feeling particularly motivated, they occasionally boil up great cauldrons of fish, flavoured with roots and herbs gathered at night in the highlands, and accompanied by a liberal sprinkling of mushrooms that they have cultivated themselves below ground.

Even young troll children have little problem with digesting whole fish, complete with heads, fins, bones and all.

AN AUTHENTIC ICELANDIC FOLK TALE

A troll woman named Kólka lived in a cave below the southern slopes of the mountain Skjaldbreið and she used to go fishing in her stone boat from Hafnabúðir near Akranes. She once saved the farmer at Hafnir from a storm at sea. When she landed with him at Grútarvík, she was so thirsty that she emptied an entire lake which has since been called Kólkutjörn (Kólka's Pool). Later on, Kólka said about her rowing exploits: "I rowed the world, I rowed high waves; I rowed myself blue, I rowed myself grey. Then I took an old woman's break, and after that got up again, ripped up my sleeves, and pulled with my head down to my knees. I'm sure that no dozen men could do better."

Molten lava streams are tapped into for cooking purposes.

Diagram showing how it is possible for trolls to fish, even in broad day light from subterranean caves.

Several folk tales tell of the sorceress's skills at preparing bait that no fish can resist. On one occasion, as thanks for help rendered, a troll woman gave Jón, a fisherman from the Westman Islands, two of her hooks. The story tells how he and his old, luckless captain rowed out to sea: "And as soon as Jón tried the hook that the troll had given him and dropped the line over the side, he immediately pulled up a fish. And this went on: the fish came up one after another."

Troll caves are warm, dark, and often humid, and are therefore the perfect environment for the cultivation of mushrooms. Trolls have nurtured and harvested mushrooms for as long as they can remember (which is quite a bit). Over the centuries, they've managed to increase the size of the mushrooms considerably, as well as controlling their texture and strengthening their pungent fungal flavours. The largest varieties of mushrooms now have thick, tough skins that are as useful and hardwearing as leather.

TROLL HIBERNATION

Sleeping is undoubtedly the most important aspect of a troll's existence. It is the reason why they live so long. Indeed, they view all waking periods as a total waste of slumber time.

This love of sleep is inherent. Trolls are naturally opposed to spending more effort on anything than is absolutely necessary. Unlike humans, they are not driven by ambition, except perhaps the aspiration to sleep as much as possible. It has been suggested, however, that trolls have some control over their dreams, and have developed this into an internal art form. For them, sleep is a little like popping out to the video-shop, only they can decide how the storyline should progress.

The best sleepers are held in great esteem by the other trolls. Since ascertaining time underground is rather problematic and because trolls in general have little interest in measuring time, it is rather difficult to determine with any accuracy just how long a troll in top form can sleep.

Troll sleep is probably more akin to animal hibernation than to human slumber. Their metabolism slows down until their breathing has become so shallow that it can hardly be perceived and their hearts have almost stopped. Once they have drifted into this state, they hardly move at all. For this reason trolls do not require beds, as humans do. They construct an individual kind of nest. Starting with a thick base of twigs and roots, they add layers of moss and leaves, and finally, for the finishing touch, put in a coating of hair, wool, fluff, spider's webs and such like. This may not be the height of comfort as we would understand it, but since they are near enough comatose when sleeping, trolls feel little discomfort.

Trolls believe that the spirits of beings, whether they be birds, fish, human or troll are retained within stone.

Trolls have a saying that "Life is something you do when you can't get to sleep." It is not that they have anything against being awake, but rather that they have a decided preference for sleep.

To encourage and enhance their slumber, trolls chisel these sleeping charms, which are then buried within the structure of the nests. They believe that this will improve their sleeping prowess.

Waking a sleeping troll can be extremely difficult, and is only ever attempted if a volcanic eruption has been predicted in the near vicinity. On such occasions, if all attempts at dragging the troll back to consciousness have failed, the sleeper is simply dragged away to safety in plenty of time. Since trolls sleep in shifts, there are always a number of them around to keep an ear to the ground for such rare emergencies. They are instinctively in tune with the moods of the rock around them, so they are rarely, if ever, caught out.

For a troll, waking up is a very slow process indeed. It can take months for an older troll to progress from the first faint flickering of an eyelid to the point at which it eventually stands up and goes off in search of breakfast.

HABITAT

Few people are aware of the fact that Icelandic trolls have their own particular troll world. They don't just live in caves scattered around the country. Iceland is a volcanic island, and over many thousands of years, volcanic eruptions and earthquakes have created an endless maze of interlinking tunnels, chutes, pits and chambers deep down below the surface of the earth. In this dark world, the trolls have made a comfortable home for themselves, a world where they live in peace and quiet in their own form of society. The rock that they live in, however, is not always as quiet as they are, and there are times when trolls find themselves faced with uncontrollable central heating problems and have to move on to find a new place of residence.

Down here in the depths, trolls can find, or fashion, most of the implements that they need for daily life. The molten lava is easily shaped into dishes, plates and other useful tools. The fires of the depths provide both light and warmth, and the seething magma pits are excellent for keeping their large cauldrons simmering.

If we measured trolls by horse-power as we do cars, the average troll would probably be estimated at an average of 7hp.

When the trolls have finished shaping their new abode, they tidy up the debris by simply emptying it out of the nearest available rock opening. When the work has been completed, they plug up the hole with the stones that remain. It is this regular cleaning up activity that accounts for the many scree slopes seen around the country.

Most trolls squat or sit cross-legged on the floor when engaged in conversation or eating. Some of the more creative trolls, however, carve out squatting platforms for themselves in their favourite corners. The designs of these pieces of furniture are often quite outrageously ostentatious.

Trolls like to keep themselves clean, and thus take long, hot spring baths at least once a century, whether they need them or not. This might not seem all that regular, but it must always be remembered that trolls are asleep most of the time. Since there are numerous underground hot springs, bathing in comfort is no problem.

Foreigners often complain about the smell of the hot water in Iceland. There is a good, if little known, reason for this. The hot water that comes out of Icelandic water taps is pumped directly out of subterranean hot springs, and it should be borne in mind that this water has probably run through several troll baths before reaching the surface. We can only hope that trolls do nothing else but wash themselves in this water.

TROLLS & PUFFINS

An intimate relationship has always existed between trolls and puffins. Indeed, trolls have purposely hollowed out spaces for themselves right behind the puffin burrows in many of the larger nesting cliffs, so as to be able to monitor the progress of the chicks and enjoy their friendly company.

At first glance, you might think there could be little connection between the sleepy, earth-bound troll, and the charming puffin. Both creatures, however, share the common characteristics of building their homes and breeding below the surface of the earth. Puffins enjoy the company of the trolls, and are known to return to the same burrows each year, for as many as thirty years.

The birds, of course, are entirely self-sufficient. Life, however, can get somewhat precarious for them when the summer storms start howling around the cliffs. These gales can rage for days on end, making it difficult, if not impossible, for the parents to head out to sea and gather food for their young. At such times, the trolls are happy to lend a helping hand. They wander down to fish from their underground caves in order to bring back large helpings of the small fry that form the puffin's staple diet. This ensures the survival of the young chicks the trolls care so much for. The main reason why the trolls keep up this odd relationship with the puffins is one of pure pleasure. For them, the puffins are an endless source of entertainment. The sound of their cooing, squawking and chattering echoes throughout the maze of caverns, filling them with what the trolls consider to be the most exquisite music.

The observation caves are excavated in the winters so as not to disturb the nesting puffins. Basalt columns are used to strengthen the structure to ensure that there are no cave-ins. When they are not attending to the puffins, the trolls block off each hole with a boulder. This grants the puffin a little privacy.

In the distant past, an evil troll was believed to live in a cave on the island of Grimsey. It was said that whenever men lowered themselves down the cliffs to catch sea-birds, a shaggy grey hand would come out and cut the ropes, causing the men to fall to their deaths. In the end, the priest Pall Tomasson was asked to bless the cliff. Pall spotted some sharp ridges jutting from the cliff which were fraying the ropes. He was attached to a rope and went down the cliff-face, secretly taking a hammer with him. He told the people to keep singing psalms loudly, until he told them to draw him up. The inhabitants of the island thus thought that Pall had blessed the cliff, but in fact he had made them sing so they wouldn´t hear him chipping the sharp ridges away from the cliff. Since that time no one has died on the ropes here.

With its flamboyantly-coloured beak and elegant dinner jacket, the puffin looks somewhat like a miniature version of a proud, feathery, orchestral conductor. Every summer, between 10 and 12 million of these birds migrate to Iceland in order to breed.

SLEEPING OUTDOORS

A great many of the Icelandic troll stories that have been passed down from antiquity end up with the trolls (who are usually described as hideous old hags or unattractive slobs) turning into stone when exposed to direct sunlight.

This has nothing to do with the ozone layer. Iceland has an abundance of curiously shaped rock formations dotted around its surface, and throughout the ages people have woven tales explaining how these rocks might have come into being. There was little else to do on the long, dark, cold winter evenings, as people huddled together safe from the winter storms.

Of course, nothing in nature reacts in this way to sun – not even Icelanders in the Canary Islands – and it is definitely not the case with trolls. What might have given rise to this misconception is that it has occasionally happened in the past that trolls, wandering around at night, have strayed too far from their cave entrance and then happened to come face to face with the rising sun. Now, being both nocturnal and subterranean, trolls are accustomed to very low levels of light. In such circumstances, the dazzle of the sun coming up will temporarily blind them, causing the trolls to sit stock still with their eyes firmly closed. This will be quite enough to lull the poor creatures off to sleep.

Once they have dropped off, trolls sleep for a very long time, and nature, as a matter of course, will quickly provide them with a camouflage. After a year or so, the trolls start to blend quite successfully with the environment. Grass and shrubs start growing in the deeper crevices, and moss and lichen wrap themselves around those places that are more exposed. And the longer the trolls sleep, the more they become one with nature. Indeed, it is technically possible for a human to walk over a sleeping troll without ever being aware of its presence.

Karl (Old Man) and Kerling (Old Woman) stand firmly in the Jökulsárgljúfur canyon not far from Vesturdalur. They lived in Tröllahellir (Troll Caves) on the east bank of the river.

The Snæfellsjökull glacier is considered to be one of the few great power centres on the planet, a place where many lines of energy come together. People from all over the world regularly meet here in the summer to reap the benefits of the power from the glacier. This is one of the few things about which trolls and humans agree. The trolls also hold festivals here, and they too tend to do this when the natural power surge is at its peak.

The raven plays a big part
in Icelandic folk tales. This
might well be the resault
of their friendship and
collaboration with the trolls.
Here we can see that they
have deliberately built a nest
to help disguise the fact that
there is a sleeping troll
beneath.

TROLLS ON THE MAP

There has been very little contact between humans and trolls over the centuries. Nonetheless, careful study of any map of Iceland will soon reveal just how deep an impact the trolls have had on the Icelandic psyche. The list of place names that directly mention trolls, or have some relation to them, is seemingly endless.

A few of these place names have been picked out here to illustrate this. Stories that human beings have spun around the standing stones found in many of these places have slanderously blackened the reputation of the essentially affable Icelandic troll.

Our hope is that this small book will go some way towards rectifying this present state of affairs and building up a greater understanding of one of the world's least known featherless bipeds.

The landscape near Svalvogar is stunning. A number of trolls have appeared from these steep cliffs.

Nubers indicate places of famous trolls from Icelandic folk tales. Location in italic.

1 Bergþór - *Bláfell*	38 Kuflungur - *Stokkseyri*
2 Bryðja - *Bryðjuskál*	39 Likný - *Þjórsárdalur*
3 Böltur - *Lásfjall*	40 Loppa - *Fnjóskadalur*
4 Elliði - *Elliðafjall*	41 Margvís/Tögld - *Hornafjörður*
5 Fenjamýrarkerling - *Svarfaðardalur*	42 Maurhildur - *Stokkseyri*
6 Flotnös - *Ingjaldssandur*	43 Mjóafjarðarskessan - *Mjóifjörður*
7 Flotsokka - *Dýrafjörður*	44 Móðar í Móðarsfelli - *Vatnsskarð*
8 Gapi - *Núpsdalur*	45 Skröggur/Skellinefja - *Hornstrandir*
9 Geira - *Myrkárdalur*	46 Skinnhetta - *Vatnsdalur*
10 Gellivör - *Staðarfjall*	47 Skráma - *Siglufjörður*
11 Gilitrutt - *Eyjafjöll*	48 Skrúðsbóndinn - *Fáskrúðsfjörður*
12 Gletta - *Glettingur*	49 Steingerður - *Kerlingarfjöll*
13 Gljúfrageir - *Háignúpur*	50 Sævar - *Sæhamar*
14 Glúmur - *Hornstrandir*	51 Valagilsskessa - *Fljótsdalshérað*
15 Gríður - *Gríðarhellir, Breiðuvík*	52 Valdi (Skuggavaldi) - *Valdadalur*
16 Grímaldur - *Þistilfjörður*	53 Þjóðbrók - *Selárdalur, Steingrímsfjörður*
17 Guðlaugur - *Guðlaugshöfði, Bitrufjörður*	54 Þórir - *Þórisvatn, Hróarstunga*
18 Gunna - *Herfell, Loðmundarfjörður*	
19 Hafnarkarl - *Höfn, Dýrafjörður*	
20 Hallgerður - *Bláfjall*	
21 Hallmundur - *Hallmundarhraun*	
22 Hetta - *Ennisfjall*	
23 Hít - *Hundahellir, Hítardalur*	
24 Hreggnasi - *Snæfellsnes*	
25 Húsagilsskessa - *Mýrdalur*	
26 Járngrímur - *Lómagnúpur*	
27 Jóra - *Jórukleif, Grafningur*	
28 Katla - *Kötlugjá, Mýrdalsjökull*	
29 Ketilþór - *Hælavíkurbjarg*	
30 Þorketill - *Hornbjarg*	
31 Kleppa - *Steingrímsfjörður*	
32 Klukka - *Klukkugil, Suðursveit*	
33 Kola - *Víðidalur*	
34 Kolbjörn - *Brattagil, Hrútafjarðardalur*	
35 Kolfreyja - *Fáskrúðsfjörður*	
36 Kólka - *Skjaldbreið*	
37 Kráka - *Bláfjall*	

The troll woman in the Kerlingarfjall apparently turned to stone with the rising of the sun. She had planned to give her boyfriend some trout to put in his stew, but was turned to stone with her bag still on her back.

Troll-like rock formations are a common sight in the Icelandic countryside. Some are relatively small. Others, like that depicted here, are enormous, and especially in human terms.

The mountains of the western fjords are a paradise for trolls. Here a troll named Jörundur can be seen standing out against the horizon.

Once upon a time, long ago, a troll couple had planned to lead their cow across Skagafjörður but they were transfixed by the daylight. It is still possible to see the old woman who was herding the cow. The old man, however, has sunk beneath the sea. The cow became Drangey island which for a long time was referred to as the "dairy cow" or "food chest" of the people of Skagafjörður, since they often used to go there to get eggs or birds to eat.

Not far from Tröllahellir is this magnificent old man or eagle that has family roots in the world of the trolls.

45 29 30
Jörundur
3 14

⁶Ísafjörður

19/7

Svalvogar

47
5

16

9

Húsavík

Drangey

Akureyri

Tröllahellir

2 40

53
31

44 4

54
10 12

15

33

18
43

8

17

13/46

37
20

Egilsstaðir

34

51

22 24

Kerlingarfjall

efellsjökull

Hofsjökull

23

49

3 5
48

21

Langjökull

52

Skessuhorn

I

36

Vatnajökull

41

Reykjavík

27

50 Höfn

39

32

42
38

26

Here it is possible to perceive a troll hauling its three-masted ship towards land. The sun rose before the troll reached the shore and so it instantly turned to stone – or so tradition has it.

ıı Mýrdalsjökull

28

25

Vík

Reynisdrangar

For many years, there was a troll woman who lived at Skessuhorn (Ogress Peak) in the Skarðsheiði moor. No one knows whether she is still alive, or exactly where she lived.